ISBN: 978-1-8384003-6-1

A CIP catalogue record for this book is available from the British Library.

BOZ PUBLICATIONS

First published by Boz Publications Ltd 2022

Boz Publications Ltd.

71-75 Shelton Street, Covent Garden, London WC2H 9JQ

office@bozpublications.com - www.bozpublications.com

WHAT IS YOUR CHRISTMAS GIFT CHARLIE FARLEY?

Written by
Elaine Slade

Illustrated by
Monika Dzikowicz

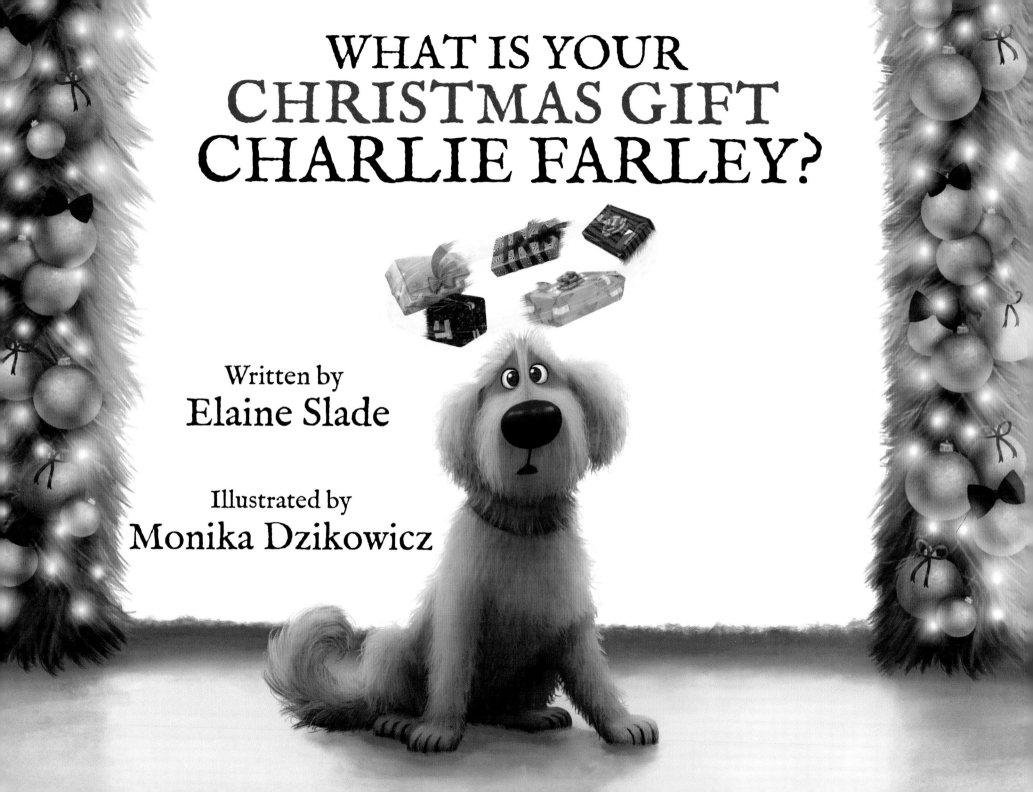

T'was that magical time of the year,
Christmas trees, sparkling lights, red-nosed reindeer.
Old songs and carols, a comforting sound,
enchantment and charm were wafting around.

Parties and pantomimes, laughter and singing,
nativities acted out, church bells a-ringing.
Santa Claus, stockings and long Christmas lists,
everyone dashing to choose perfect gifts.

WHAT IS YOUR CHRISTMAS GIFT CHARLIE FARLEY?

Jasper tucked up, asleep in his bed,
dreaming of presents, all shiny and red.
All sorted and ordered, stacked up very neat,
gift wrapping and labelling already complete.

Charlie Farley lay sprawled, flaked out in his bed,
whilst visions of gifts spun around in his head.
What could he give the dogs to impress?
Such high expectations,
OH DEAR, FEEL THE STRESS!

Christmas had come, all was arranged,
Jasper's friends they all met, their gifts were exchanged.
Oh, the cries of delight, exclamations and praise,
each one secretly hoping their gift would amaze!

Charlie Farley, too late with his untidy mind,
his thoughts they unravelled, no sense could he find!
He struggled and strove but ideas would not come,
trying hard to impress just made him glum!

He muttered, he scuttered,
he paced to and fro.

He sputtered, he stuttered,
ideas would not flow!

Why could he not give
perfect gifts like Jasper?

Along came Winnie with a clatter and a bump,
'What are <u>you</u> doing for presents?'
she enquired with a jump.

Charlie shuffled round and replied with a sigh,
'I've left it too late to know what to buy!'

Charlie meandered in circles whilst he thought
'We haven't the money to buy what they've bought!'

'Let's think what we _have got_' Winnie dog said and a thought popped up into Charlie's head!

WHAT IS YOUR CHRISTMAS GIFT CHARLIE FARLEY?

'Remember we don't have to impress to succeed,
think about things our friends actually need.
A ball, bowl of water, a toy, an old shoe,
some dog treats, a game, muddy puddles too!!'

Can you find these presents
on the next page?

They raced round collecting these odds and those ends,
and put on a TREASURE HUNT, just for their friends.
Their pals dashed excitedly following clues,
breathtaking fun, they were all SO amused.

The stress and the strain to find the best present,
missed the care behind giving, to make Christmas pleasant.
A gift from the heart Charlie had found
was the treasure needed for friends to resound...

WHAT A PERFECT
CHRISTMAS GIFT
CHARLIE FARLEY!!

THE END

What are YOUR Christmas gifts to your family and friends?

Giving from the heart is what we recommend.
Draw your present idea and the person
you'd like to give it to here.

Can **YOU** draw gifts and colour
a **TREASURE HUNT** just for **YOUR** friends?

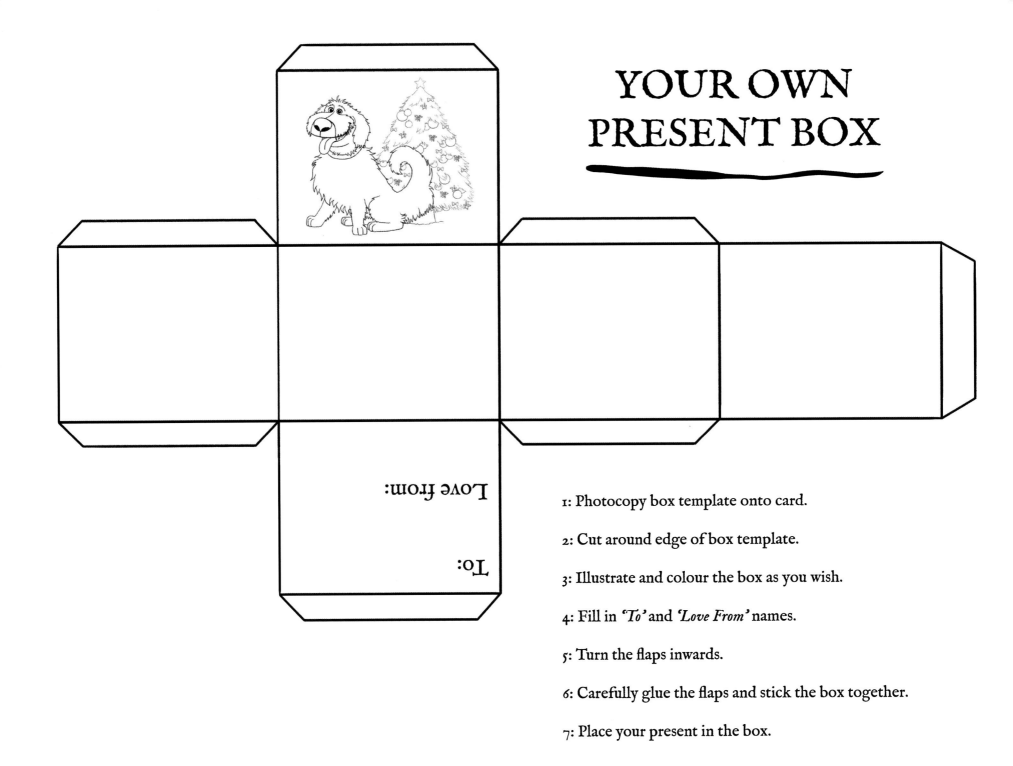

YOUR OWN PRESENT BOX

Love from:

To:

1: Photocopy box template onto card.

2: Cut around edge of box template.

3: Illustrate and colour the box as you wish.

4: Fill in 'To' and 'Love From' names.

5: Turn the flaps inwards.

6: Carefully glue the flaps and stick the box together.

7: Place your present in the box.

HAPPY CHRISTMAS!

Colour, cut out, give to someone for Christmas.

CHARLIE'S ACTIVITY GUIDE!
- to help children explore giving from the heart, rather than giving to impress -

Complete the page *'What are your Christmas Gifts to your family and friends?'* together.
Encourage them to think about something they could make or use as a gift.

Photocopy the *Box Template* on card, cut out, decorate and stick together for them to use as a gift box.
Enlarge the photocopy if you want a larger box.

Photocopy the *Christmas Mat*, encourage your child to colour carefully,
laminate and wrap as a gift for a family member or for your child to use at Christmas.

Photocopy and children colour the *Treasure Hunt* page, then encourage your child to think
of simple gifts they could draw on the page for others to find, draw them in the picture
(older children will be able to draw a half hidden present).

Write and decorate an acrostic poem around someone's name as a Christmas gift
of encouragement for them to stick on their wall, e.g. *C (Caring) L (Loveable) A (Active) R (Reliable) E (Encouraging)*.
Use a thesaurus or look up on the internet for words.

For older children discuss whether they could make *'kindness vouchers'*.
Could they promise to tidy their room, wash the dishes or phone Grandma once a week?
Consider with them whether the task is achievable; introduce them to the phrase
'better to under promise and over deliver than over promise and under deliver!'

Look at words in the story that your child might not have understood e.g. enchantment, nativities, sprawled,
exchanged, unravelled, enquired, meandered. Look up the meanings together.

Discuss with your child/ren or as a family that sometimes you already have enough and consider the concept
of giving to others through a charity or to a family or elderly person nearby who are in need or lonely.
Could they bake Christmas biscuits or mince pies for neighbours? (Check on allergies before giving!)

JASPER'S MESSAGE TO PARENTS AND TEACHERS.

Before reading the book:

- What can you see on the front cover? How do we know it is Christmas time?
- How is Charlie Farley feeling?
- Does the blurb on the back cover tell us any more about why his head is in a spin?

Whilst reading the book:

- Encourage your child/ren to join in *'What's your Christmas Gift Charlie Farley?'* and *'What a perfect Christmas gift Charlie Farley!'*
- *'T'was that magical time of the year...'* Can you find the aspects of Christmas mentioned in the text
- *'T'was that magical time of the year...'* Do you recognise any of the characters in the Market Square?
- *'Parties and Pantomimes...'* Everyone looks happy except one character... who is that and why?
- *'Jasper tucked up...'* How is Jasper feeling about his presents? Is he worried? How do you know?
- *'Jasper tucked up...'* Before you turn the page ask your child to predict how Charlie will be feeling on the next page.
- *'Charlie Farley lay sprawled...'* Were you right? What is the problem?
- *'Christmas had come...'* Why was Charlie hiding behind the tree?
- *'Charlie Farley, too late...'* He had a lovely present from Jasper, was Charlie happy now? Why not?
- *'Let's think what we have got!'* Why does Charlie Farley suddenly look happy?
- *'They raced round collecting...'* Can you find the treasure from the page before in the picture? Look carefully!
- Which part of the story did you like best? Why was that?

Questions to help explore giving from the heart rather than to impress:

- How does this story begin? How does it end? How does it change?
- Which gifts were best, Charlie's or Jasper's? Why do you think that?
- Have you ever felt that someone else gave better gifts than you? OR that someone else receives better gifts than you?
- Explore how giving to impress makes *'you'* feel more important, whereas giving from the heart focuses on the *'other'* person.

THE
CHARLIE FARLEY
SERIES

DON'T
BE SCARED
CHARLIE
FARLEY!

Written by
Elaine Slade

Illustrated by
Monika Dzikowicz

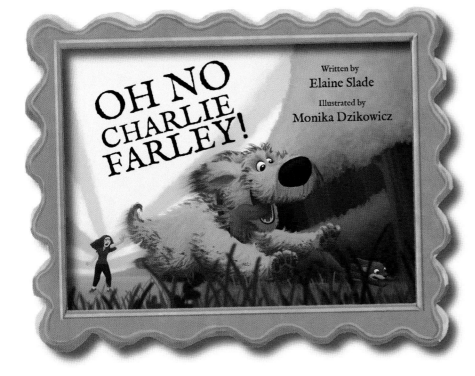

OH NO
CHARLIE
FARLEY!

Written by
Elaine Slade

Illustrated by
Monika Dzikowicz

AVAILABLE AT:

www.elainesladebooks.com

www.bozpublications.com

& your local independent bookstore

Written by
Elaine Slade
Illustrated by
Monika Dzikowicz

YOU
CAN'T PLAY
CHARLIE
FARLEY!

Written by   Illustrated by
Elaine Slade   Monika Dzikowicz

IT'S OKAY
TO FEEL SAD
CHARLIE
FARLEY!

'MAYBE I
CAN' SAID
CHARLIE FARLEY!

COMING SOON

Elaine Slade
- Author -

Elaine is a former Deputy Head who loves exploring a good story and inspiring children, including her own family (four daughters, two granddaughters) to love reading. She is passionate about equipping children to face life positively and raising their self-esteem. Elaine loves the season of Christmas and the magical feeling of giving from the heart to others, as she was taught to enjoy doing as a young child.

www.elainesladebooks.com

Monika Dzikowicz
- Illustrator -

Monika is a Polish illustrator who is passionate about stories that empower people to embrace their emotions and give them the strength to change their life for the better.

www.monikadzikowicz.com

And meet the REAL
Charlie Farley & Jasper

Dedicated to my Mum and Dad
who taught me from an early
age the joy of giving to others
in need at Christmas.
Elaine

THANK YOU TO EVERYONE
WHO SHARED THEIR CHRISTMAS WITH ME.
YOU GAVE ME THE BEST GIFTS OF ALL:
KINDNESS AND GOOD COMPANY...
...AND DELICIOUS POLISH FOOD.
WITH LOVE, MONIKA ♡